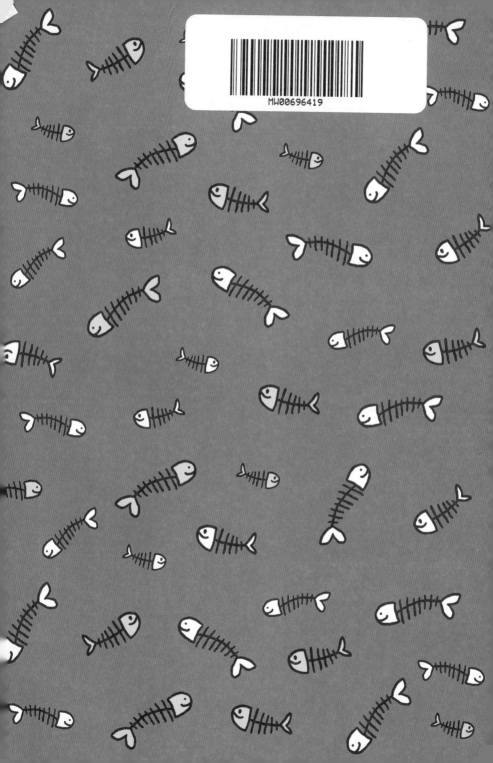

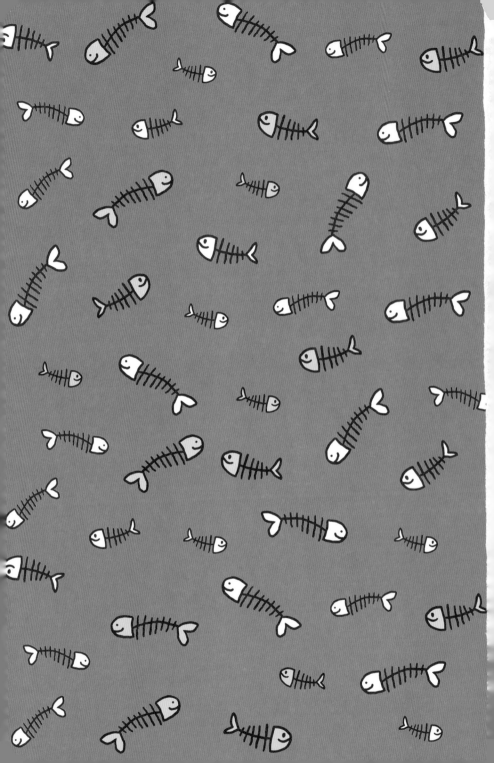

Created and published by Knock Knock
1635-B Electric Avenue
Venice, CA 90291
knockknockstuff.com

Illustrations by Gemma Correll

ISBN: 978-160106678-7
UPC: 825703-50134-6

10 9 8 7 6 5 4 3

100 REASONS TO PANIC

ABOUT BEING A

CAT LADY

A JOURNAL FOR THE FELINE-OBSESSED

KNOCK KNOCK®

VENICE, CALIFORNIA

10-29-15   2.13.1 16s

#1. YOU'LL SHOW STRANGERS PHOTOS OF YOUR CAT.*

*It's payback for oohing and ahhing over all those baby photos.

#2. YOU'LL GIVE YOUR CAT SILLY NICKNAMES LIKE PROFESSOR SNUGGLEPAWS AND FURRY MCFUZZERSON.*

*He has nicknames for you, too. They're not as cute.

DATE: _____ / _____ / _____

#3. YOU'LL SET UP VIDEO FEEDS SO YOU CAN WATCH YOUR CAT FROM WORK.*

*And then you'll finally know how she fills her days.

DATE: _____/_____/_____

#4. CATS CAN'T FILL THE EMPTINESS INSIDE.*

*Oh, wait. Yes, they can.

#5. YOUR CAT iS ALWAYS STARiNG AT YOU.*

*Actually, he's judging you.

DATE: _____/_____/_____

#6. YOUR CAT WILL PEE ON YOUR STUFF.*

*You probably needed to replace those slippers anyway.

DATE: _____/_____/_____

#7. YOUR FRIENDS WITH ALLERGIES WON'T WANT TO COME OVER.*

*You have enough human friends.

#8. HOW MANY CATS iS TOO MANY CATS?*

*Once you no longer need bed coverings, it's time to stop.

DATE: _____/_____/_____

#9. YOU CAN'T TAKE A CAT FOR A WALK.*

*You won't have to wait while he pees on another bush, either.

_____

_____

_____

_____

_____

_____

_____

_____

_____

_____

_____

_____

_____

_____

_____

_____

_____

_____

_____

_____

_____

_____

_____

_____

_____

_____

- -

#10. YOU'LL REFER TO YOUR CAT AS YOUR BABY.*

*She *is* your baby—your fur baby.

#11. PEOPLE WILL START GIVING YOU CAT MUGS.*

*Wine + cat mug = classy!

DATE: _____/_____/_____

#12. YOUR CAT WILL PRESENT YOU WITH DEAD MICE AS GIFTS.*

*Cats give you gifts.

#13. CATS ARE ALOOF.*

*They prefer "discriminating."

#15. ALL YOUR CLOTHES WILL BE COVERED IN CAT HAIR.*

*Is there a more perfect accessory for your "I ♥ CATS" sweatshirt?

#16. YOU'LL GET WEIRD AND START MAKING STUFF OUT OF "FOUND" CAT FUR.*

*You're upcycling.

#17. YOU'LL NEVER REALLY UNDERSTAND YOUR CAT.*

*You'll never be bored by predictability.

#18. A CAT WON'T DEFEND YOUR HOME LIKE A DOG MIGHT.*

*Instead, a cat might break into your home. Cats are crafty like that.

DATE: _____/_____/_____

_____

_____

_____

_____

_____

_____

_____

_____

_____

_____

_____

_____

_____

_____

_____

_____

_____

_____

_____

_____

_____

_____

_____

- -

#19. YOU'LL DRESS UP YOUR CAT.*

*Where do you think the expression "cat's pajamas" came from?

DATE: _____/_____/_____

#20. A CUTE KITTEN CAN TURN INTO AN UGLY CAT.*

*But she'll be your ugly cat.

#21. ALL THAT LEAPiNG HAS YOU WORRiED YOUR CAT WiLL PLUNGE TO HiS DEATH.*

*He has nine lives. Duh.

DATE: _____/_____/_____

#22. YOU'LL START COLLECTING CATS.*

*They're cuter than comic books.

DATE: _____ / _____ / _____

#23. PURRING iS SORT OF CREEPY.*

*It's your cat's version of applause. The louder he purrs, the more adequate he considers you.

#24. CATS HOLD GRUDGES.*

*Easy solution: do not cross a cat.

#25. YOU'LL SUBSCRIBE TO *CAT FANCY.* *

*You can finally cancel those subscriptions to *Living Alone* and *Basketweaving Monthly.*

DATE: _____/_____/_____

#26. YOUR CAT WILL CONSTANTLY FOLLOW YOU AROUND THE HOUSE.*

*You'll never be lonely.

DATE: _____/_____/_____

#27. YOUR CAT WILL HOG THE BED.*

*Less sleep means more time to get things done.

DATE: _____/_____/_____

#28. YOU'LL PREFER HANGING OUT WITH YOUR CAT.*

*Well, he *is* the best company.

#29. CATS HAVE SUCH AN ATTITUDE.*

*They prefer "cattitude."

#30. YOUR CAT LICKS YOU—AND YOU HATE THAT FEELING.*

*She thinks the same thing about you. Wait, you lick your cat?

#31. YOU'LL HAVE TO CATPROOF YOUR HOME.*

*Don't bother—you can't outsmart a cat.

#32. HAIRBALLS ARE DISGUSTING.*

*They camouflage dust bunnies quite well.

#33. SCRATCHING POSTS ARE UGLY.*

*You can start a line of Eames-inspired cat accessories.

#34. YOUR CAT WILL END UP ADDICTED TO CATNIP.*

*Cat twelve-step programs are a great place to make friends.

SIR FLUFFINGTON

#35. YOU'LL COMMISSION MULTIPLE PORTRAITS OF YOUR CAT.*

*You'll be a patron of the arts.

DATE: _____/_____/_____

DATE: _____ / _____ / _____

#36. YOU CAN'T TRAIN A CAT.*

*Being a drill sergeant is no fun, anyway.

DATE: _____/_____/_____

#37. CATS ARE BORN KILLERS.*

*You'll have on-call pest control.

#38. CATS ARE HIGH-MAINTENANCE.*

*So are you.

DATE: _____/_____/_____

#39. CATS DON'T REALLY DO ANYTHING.*

*Finally, a living thing that doesn't want anything from you.

#40. YOU'LL THROW BIRTHDAY PARTIES FOR YOUR CAT.*

*In return, he will give you the gift of tolerating your existence.

DATE: _____/_____/_____

#41. YOUR CAT WILL MEOW CONSTANTLY.*

*Those meows will drown out annoying car alarms, street noise, and loud neighbors.

DATE: _____/_____/_____

_____

_____

_____

_____

_____

_____

_____

_____

_____

_____

_____

_____

_____

_____

_____

_____

_____

_____

_____

_____

_____

_____

#42. YOUR CAT WILL NEVER ASK ABOUT YOUR DAY.*

*You won't have to listen to tedious stories about her day, either.

#43. YOUR CAT WILL ESCAPE, CLIMB A TREE, AND NEVER COME DOWN.*

*You'll have to call a hunky firefighter to rescue the cat.

#44. YOU'LL CALL YOURSELF "CAT MOMMY."*

*Your cat will call you "the one who feeds me."

#45. YOUR CAT HAS A COOL LITERARY NAME, AND NO ONE GETS IT.*

*You'll have a reason to expound upon the greatness of the classics.

#46. KITTY LITTER IS GROSS.*

*At least you won't have to take your cat out at two in the morning when he's gotta go.

DATE: _____ / _____ / _____

#47. YOUR CAT WON'T WANT TO CURL UP WITH YOU ON A RAINY DAY.*

*That's called respecting your personal space.

#48. YOUR TOILET PAPER WiLL END UP SHREDDED TO BiTS.*

*But the joy it'll bring your cat will be priceless.

DATE: _____/_____/_____

#49. YOUR CAT WILL HIDE UNDER THE BED FOR MOST OF HER WAKING HOURS.*

*You won't have to make any awkward small talk.

DATE: _____/_____/_____

#50. YOUR HOME WILL SMELL LIKE CAT PEE.*

*You'll have an excuse to buy fancy candles. Lots of them.

DATE: _____ / _____ / _____

_____

_____

_____

_____

_____

_____

_____

_____

_____

_____

_____

_____

_____

_____

_____

_____

_____

_____

_____

_____

- -

#51. YOU'LL FEEL GUILTY LEAVING YOUR CAT ALONE ALL DAY.*

*Think of how excited she'll be when you return. (She won't notice.)

DATE: _____ / _____ / _____

#52. YOU'LL RECORD A TON OF CAT VIDEOS.*

*Viral stardom is mere clicks away.

#53. YOUR CAT THINKS EVERYTHING IS A TOY CREATED EXPRESSLY FOR HIM.*

*Playing together relieves his stress—and yours.

#54. CAT FOOD iS STiNKY.*

*That annoying guy at work who heats up fish
in the microwave will now make you feel right at home.

DATE: _____/_____/_____

#55. YOU'LL SEND HOLIDAY CARDS FROM YOU AND YOUR CAT.*

*You'll have something to do with all the photos you take of her.

DATE: _____ / _____ / _____

DATE: _____ / _____ / _____

#56. YOUR ONLY CONVERSATION TOPIC: YOUR CAT.*

*Hey, you're having conversations.

#57. YOU'LL START TO DISLIKE DOGS.*

*Dogs will love you regardless.

#58. YOUR CAT WILL BE A BULLY.*

*You can put up a "Beware of Cat" sign—and mean it.

#59. CATS EXPECT TO BE WORSHIPPED.*

*They come by it rightly; the cat goddess Bastet inspired a cult in ancient Egypt.

DATE: _____/_____/_____

#60. YOUR NEW CAT WON'T GET ALONG WITH YOUR OLD CAT.*

*But they might start fighting over your affection. Flattering!

DATE: _____/_____/_____

#61. YOUR CAT WiLL ALWAYS DEMAND YOUR ATTENTiON.*

*Someone needs you!

#62. YOUR CAT WILL ALWAYS WANT TO SLEEP IN YOUR FRESHLY WASHED LAUNDRY.*

*When you wash your clothes again, they'll be extra-clean!

#63. VET VISITS ARE EXPENSIVE.*

*You needed to get on a budget anyway.

#64. YOU'LL GET CARPAL TUNNEL FROM PETTING YOUR CAT.*

*He'll never feel unloved.

#65. YOUR CAT WILL WAKE YOU UP TOO EARLY IN THE MORNING.*

*She's cuter than an alarm clock, isn't she?

#66. YOU CAN'T HAVE JUST ONE CAT.*

*The more, the merrier!

#67. YOUR CAT WILL GET INTO YOUR KNITTING PROJECTS.*

*His creativity will give you something to brag about.

#68. IF YOU LIVE WITH YOUR SISTER AND A BUNCH OF CATS, YOU MIGHT BE DANGEROUSLY CLOSE TO *GREY GARDENS* TERRITORY.*

*Maybe someone will make a documentary about you.

DATE: _____/_____/_____

#69. YOUR CAT WILL ONLY DRINK OUT OF THE SINK.*

*You'll never let the dirty dishes pile up.

#70. YOU'LL NEVER BE ABLE TO FIND A CAT-SITTER YOU CAN TRUST.*

*Think of the money you'll save when you only take staycations.

#71. YOU'LL GET A TATTOO OF YOUR CAT.*

*In twenty years, you'll probably still like your cat. Can you say that about a butterfly?

#72. CATS WILL SCRATCH UP YOUR COUCH.*

*Covering it in plastic will make it easier to wipe up spills.

#73. WHEN YOU WANT TO ORDER TAKEOUT, IT'S ALWAYS SUSHI, SUSHI, SUSHI.*

*Your omega-3 levels will skyrocket.

‎ ‎

#74. CAT-OWNER STEREOTYPES ARE NOT FLATTERING.*

*As long as you're not also a hoarder and a spinster, you're fine!

DATE: _____/_____/_____

#75. YOUR CAT WILL ONLY WANT TO WATCH NATURE SHOWS ABOUT AVIAN SPECIES.*

*Birdwatching: your new shared hobby.

DATE: _____/_____/_____

#76. YOU'LL NEVER BE ALONE.*

*You'll never be alone.

DATE: ____/____/____

#77. YOUR CAT LACKS AMBITION.*

*If you could spend your days basking in the sun, wouldn't you?

DATE: _____/_____/_____

#78. YOUR CAT WILL EAT YOUR PLANTS.*

*She's trying to simplify your routines.

#79. YOU'LL GO BROKE INVESTING IN ORGANIC, CHEMICAL-FREE, PRESERVATIVE-FREE CAT PRODUCTS.*

*At least one of you is eating well.

DATE: _____/_____/_____

_____

_____

_____

_____

_____

_____

_____

_____

_____

_____

_____

_____

_____

_____

_____

_____

_____

_____

_____

_____

_____

#80. YOU'LL DRESS EXCLUSIVELY IN LEOPARD AND CHEETAH PRINTS.*

*A signature look is a sign of strong personal style.

_____

_____

_____

_____

_____

_____

_____

_____

_____

_____

_____

_____

_____

_____

_____

_____

_____

_____

_____

_____

_____

_____

_____

_____

- -

#81. IT'S HARD TO BRUSH A CAT.*

*But easier than brushing out the tangles in a squirming toddler's hair.

DATE: _____/_____/_____

#82. YOUR CAT WILL GET SICK EVERY WINTER.*

*Is there anything cuter than a cat sneezing?

DATE: _____/_____/_____

#83. IT'S HARD TO CLIP A CAT'S CLAWS.*

*Scars are an instant conversation starter.

DATE: _____/_____/_____

#84. YOUR CAT-LESS FRIENDS JUST DON'T UNDERSTAND HOW HARD IT IS TO RAISE CATS.*

*They also don't understand unconditional love, the poor things.

DATE: _____ / _____ / _____

#85. ALL THOSE CATS WiLL SCARE OFF POTENTiAL SUiTORS.*

*Who needs a suitor? You've got a ton of cats.

#86. HAVING A CAT IS LESS SOCIAL THAN HAVING A DOG.*

*It's a perfect excuse to stay in your pajamas and watch movies all day.

#87. YOU'LL ALWAYS BE VACUUMING UP FUR.*

*You'll be able to eat off your floors.

DATE: _____/_____/_____

#88. YOU'LL NEVER PLEASE YOUR CAT.*

*You won't. But your efforts will entertain him.

DATE: _____/_____/_____

MEOOOWWW
@!#Z:2?~!!&!
MEEEEOOOOW
^@#?$!

#89. YOUR CAT WILL NEVER SHUT UP.*

*And you'll learn another language: Cat.

#90. WHENEVER YOU'RE READING THE NEWSPAPER, YOUR CAT WANTS TO SIT ON TOP OF iT.*

*Goodbye gloom and doom—hello, sweet furry face!

DATE: _____/_____/_____

#91. YOUR CAT WILL EAT ALL OF YOUR FANCY CHEESE.*

*Teaching him to diet will prepare him for cat pageants.

#92. ALL YOUR HARD-EARNED MONEY WILL GO TO CAT TOYS.*

*Your cat will be most excited about the empty boxes.

#93. THE PAW-KNEADING ACROSS YOUR BODY WILL GET ANNOYING.*

*Daily massages sound kind of nice.

#94. CAT SCRATCHES HURT.*

*Better your arms than your couch.

DATE: _____ / _____ / _____

SINGING CAT

#95. YOUR CAT'S NOT AS TALENTED AS THE CATS YOU SEE ON THE INTERNET.*

*Neither of you will have to deal with the pressures of fame.

#96. YOU'LL START TAKING iN FERAL CATS.*

*You can get nonprofit status as a wildlife refuge.

#97. WHAT IF THE WORLD ENDS AND IT'S JUST YOU AND YOUR CAT?*

*Cats are excellent hunters. You'll never starve.

#98. DOG PEOPLE ACT SUPERIOR.*

*Is there a more codependent animal than the slobbery hound?

#99. CAT LADIES AREN'T SEXY.*

*What about Catwoman?

#100. YOU WON'T BE ABLE TO RELATE TO NON-CAT PEOPLE.*

*Why bother?

DATE: _____ / _____ / _____

DATE: _____ / _____ / _____

*DON'T WORRY.
YOUR FURRY ONE'S WORTH IT.

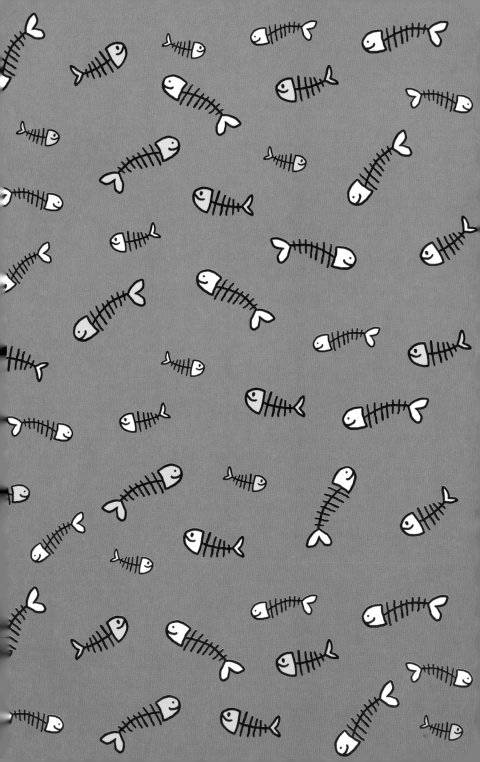

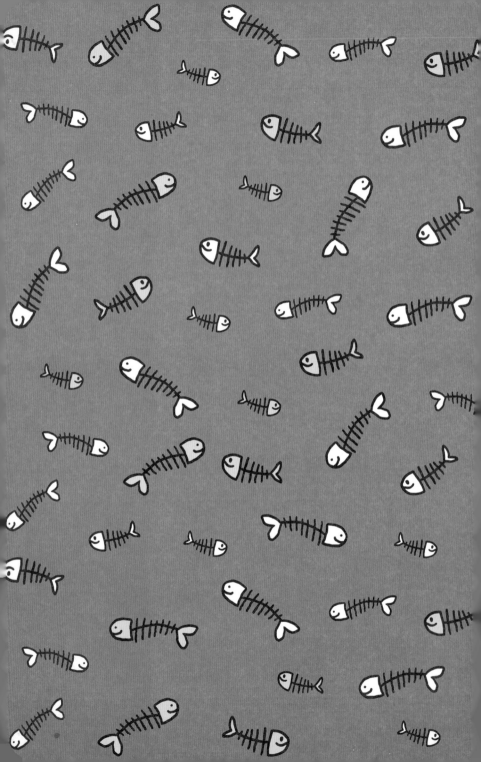